MODERN TOSS VII
*from *hitflap*

by Jon Link and Mick Bunnage

Modern Toss: PO Box 386, Brighton, BN1 3SN, United Kingdom
email: info@moderntoss.com   www.moderntoss.com
First printed up in the year of 2011

© modern toss 2011

Mr Tourette

MASTER SIGNWRITER

I need a sign to re-brand this pub I just bought, I'm chucking out all the carpet and banging up the prices to keep out the old people, this will allow me to sell scotch eggs on big white plates for 12 quid

what I might do here is reference your original branding but add a modern twist

It's a strong blend of old and new, I just don't know if it's an image people will want in their heads when they're eating food

I haven't stuck the painting of it up yet, make your mind up after that

DESPERATE BUSINESS

celebrity book signing

Pete Peters
Vigilante Shit Stirrer

yeah I've got home with a big lump of broccoli which I've paid for by weight . I've eaten the tip but I've still got the stalk which i dont want

if I bring that back in now , you weigh it and deduct it from the bill, I've kept the receipt cos I could see this happening a mile off, I paid for it on a card so if you could put the money straight back into my account I don't want to be wandering about with a load of cash

yeah mate rang up a bit earlier about the broccoli rebate. yeah forget it the dogs eaten it .

LIBERTY TAKER

alright mate, just having a shit down your chimney

work

fucking weirdo

alright mate, I got a wedding to go to at the weekend, can I borrow your wife and kids, I don't want to turn up there on me own and have people think I'm some sort of fucking weirdo

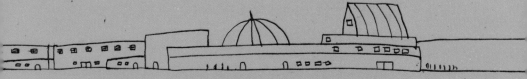

customer
sevices

Drive by Abuser considers The Chair

Square wooden platform, supported by four sticks
with an upright plank acting as a back rest,
sometimes with arm supports, sometimes without yeah
often covered in a patterned cloth of some sort
or completely moulded out of plastic.
Whatever the fuck you're made out of
you're always there helping people maintain a position,
halfway between standing up and lying down.
Try doing that without a chair,
probably end up shitting yourself after six seconds
see you round yeah

DESPERATE BUSINESS

DESPERATE BUSINESS

home~clubber

Mr Tourette

MASTER SIGNWRITER

hi Mr Tourette we're opening a non-specific, digital communications multi-platform media collective and we need a sign or something but keep it loose as the business may develop into different areas depending on if anyone pays us any money

yes for instance Dave here used to have a successful gutter cleaning firm, which may prove a useful safety net in these uncertain times

fucking arseholes sounds like a cash upfront job to me

Later...

SUPERSONIC BULLSHIT WAGON

excellent! I can see this serving us well for many years to come

yeah it works for the gutter cleaning aswell

yes it seems to be saying something, but also saying fuck all at the same time

Pete Peters
Vigilante Shit Stirrer

awkward cunt

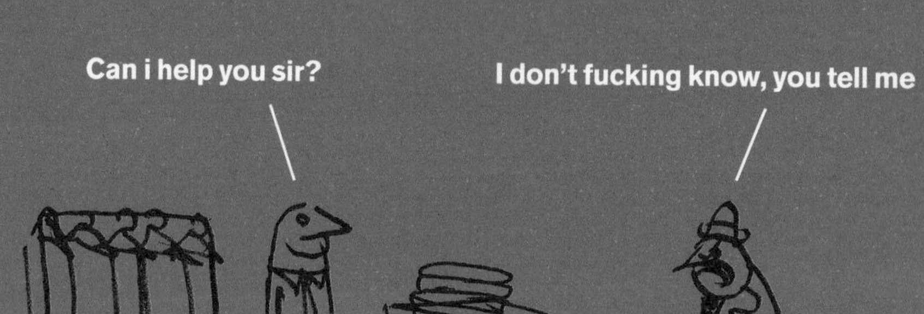

DESPERATE BUSINESS

Alright, I'm thinking of watching the London marathon on telly, do you want to sponsor me?

health

home~clubber

DESPERATE BUSINESS

legal longshots

home~clubber

Mr Tourette

MASTER SIGNWRITER

I need a sign for my living statue act, I've mastered the art of getting paid for doing fuck all whilst dressed up as an authentic suffragette woman from the victorian era

what do you do when somone puts money in?

I stick me tongue out quick like a lizard

Later...

HISTORICAL HUMAN ARSEHOLE ACT

interestingly enough I can do a 12 hour shift without a shit break, but I didn't think it was worth mentioning on the sign

yeah cheers, in my opinion that's the main thing you've got going for you

work

PEANUT

HAVING HOSPITALISED THEIR OWN SINGER, DAVID AND PAUL OF VOLATILE MOD SUPERGROUP PEANUT ARE SITTING ABOUT WRITING LYRICS..

GARY
LEAD
VOCALS

PAUL
DRUMS

DAVID
BASS

work

LIBERTY TAKER

DESPERATE BUSINESS

I've got your wages here but I'd like to offer you all
double or nothing on a fist fight in the car park

home~clubber

DESPERATE BUSINESS

Pete Peters
Vigilante Shit Stirrer

flashing lights, shooting pain in left leg, randomized vomiting, allergy to nut products, lactose intolerance, dizziness, high and low blood pressure, claustrophobic amnesia, any hint of a queue and i black out so get me on early with the wheelchairs and that, I've also got a rare form of narcolepsy where I dream I can't sleep, fear of moving objects, that includes just thinking about 'em, inability to go to toilet unless both me feet are on the ground, i might experiment with putting a couple of pre cut turf slices under me feet on that one so we should be alright in the air, narrow arteries, hypertension, fear of horses, that includes photos of them so you might wanna check your in flight brochure and rip out anything dodgy, er blinding headaches otherwise thats about it..

I'm thinking about booking a flight on your airline to Spain or somewhere and reading through the small print it says i've got to declare any medical conditions. have you got a pen handy? right here we go...

i bet you're thinking we've got a right one here yeah! Probably you're best bet is to put me in a cage or a coma, yeah. Oh while i'm here can i check your end of year accounts before i book me ticket to make sure you're not going to go tits up before we even take off,

tell you what love, i've just noticed you've got a horse as your logo, so i'm going to have to pull out of that deal, better go i'm about to black out, hope you're happy with yourself

TOTAL FUCKING DISASTER *in* 'Petrol Station'

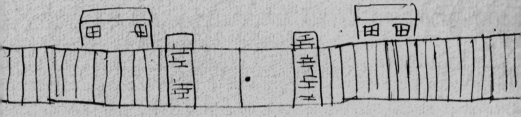

Mr Tourette
MASTER SIGNWRITER'S

Hello Mr Tourette I need a sign for my new top end, gated community development aimed at rich people who want to live next door to footballers and celebrity hairdressers

You're playing my fucking tune. Give me 20 minutes

DELUXE CUNT CAGE

um I like it. It acknowledges my clients' status while sounding reassuring on security matters

Cheers, how about if I stick a few villagers heads on poles as a warning

Sir Paul Pot
CEO & Chairman

Drive by Abuser considers The Mouth

You a mouth yeah?
stuck on the front of a face
normally down the bottom innit
Words coming out
Food going in
keep it that way round
or you'll get in a right fucking mess

customer services

Pete Peters
Vigilante Shit Stirrer

alright, yeah I'm thinking about visiting your supermarket on the way back from my morning jog

I like to finish off with a big sprint, and I'm just wondering what is the fastest speed I can run at the automatic doors without knocking meself clean fucking out? if you could get back to me that would be great, I'll be running out the door in just under 2 minutes.

ok so just to let you know that no one has got back to me so I'm going to wear a crash helmet, just don't come crying to me if I come flying through your fucking window like Matt Damon in the Bourne trilogy, thank you.

DESPERATE BUSINESS

yeah we don't actually pay a pension here, what we do is offer new employees the opportunity to whack their wages down on a 7 horse accumulator

I don't want to rush you but the first race is at 2.45

awkward cunt

TRAVEL AGENT

where would like to go sir?

you fucking tell me

relationships

work

health

I want to go on the waiting list for every operation going, I'm bound to need something done at some point and I don't want to piss about waiting for you cunts to get your act together

DESPERATE BUSINESS

Mr Tourette

MASTER SIGNWRITER

I need a sign for my stall? I was wracking my brain for an idea to base an international business around, then I thought fuck it I'll just do a cupcake stall yeah ? then I couldn't think of what to call it, ideally something to do with cupcakes and maybe get the word 'stall' in there somewhere?

this is what I call a blank canvas problem, leave it with me

Later...

yeah to be honest I couldn't be fucked to think of anything so I just did the first phrase that popped into me head with the word 'cake' in it

yeah cheers I'll probably pack it in next week, I might go and live in Thailand for a couple of years

'CAKED IN FUCKING SHIT'

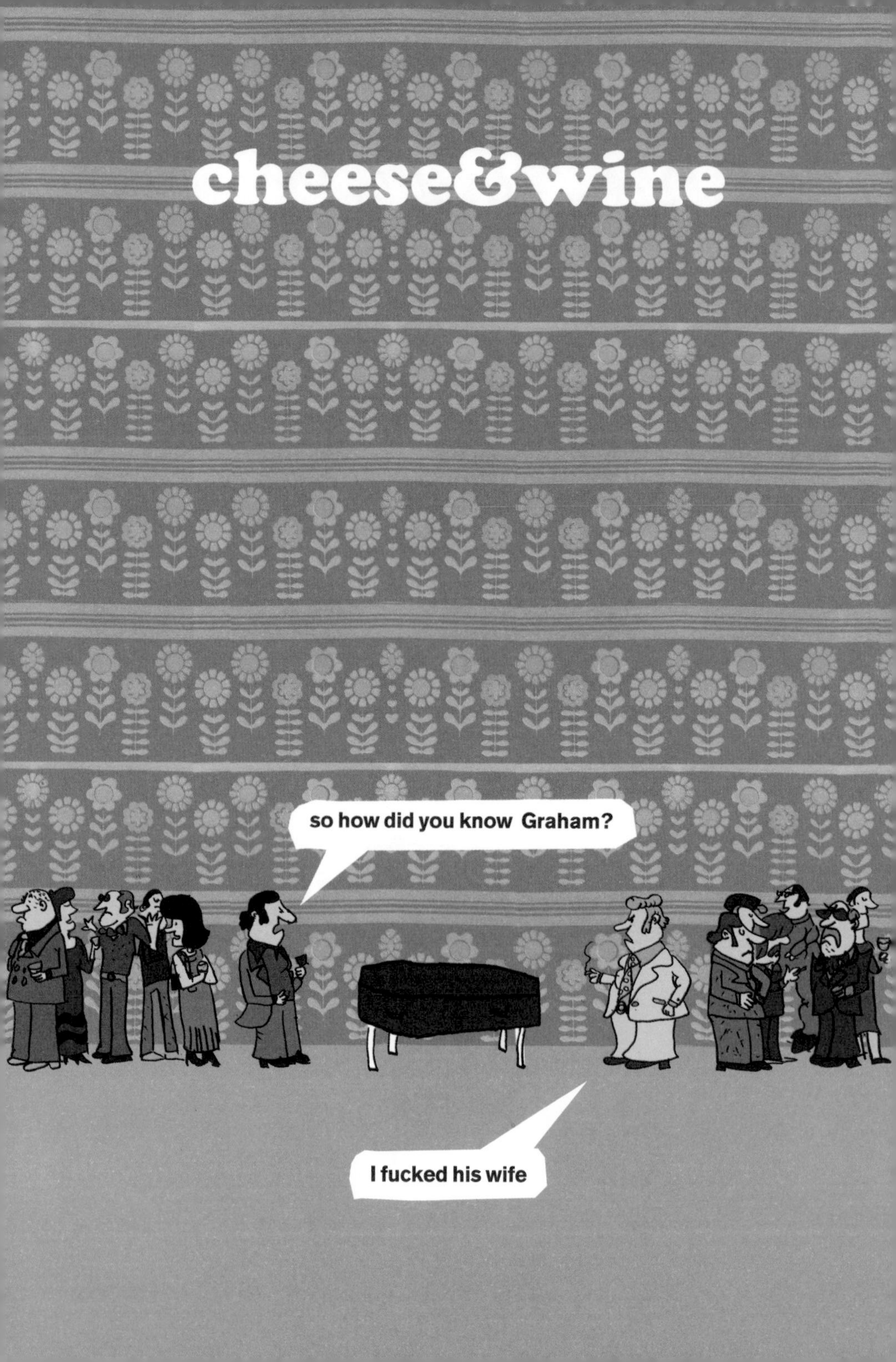
cheese&wine
so how did you know Graham?
I fucked his wife

Pete Peters
Vigilante Shit Stirrer

Alan in "Festival Weekend"

first day job enquiry

customer services

DESPERATE BUSINESS

hello I was just in the area and wondered if I could interest you in a pole dance?

Isaac Gerald William Mawson, Helen Melon Gravy Graves, Flubster, Sheepie, Trotsky & Barry Baaa, Alan Phela, Ilona McLeish, joe&helsinoz, Jerry Perkins, Juliet Cromwell, Nik Margolis, Ben Money, Pirran "the Lie" and Patrick "the Trick" Driver, Lisa Baker, Lord Ham and Lady Tree, Andrew Wanky Buns Jeffrey, Ben Collier, Alannotthatala, Little Rhysie, Aaron, Anna Hyde, All@ink_d gallery, Taylor-Cotter, the read family, Rob Curtis, Ben Rowe, The Forestry Tools, Gary Hughes, Luke Raddy, Darren Smith, Jim Christian, Maria 'Kiki Deadloss' Kikillos, Charlie Cha Cha Le Bona Abbott, Ed Richards, Richard Milne, Charles Abbott, Matt Dixon, Lisa 'Orange Sticker' Riddled Liddle, James Brown, Dan Rebellato, Shane Allen, Joseph N Samuel, Casualties of a Lifestyle, John Stune, Kaitlyn Pearson innit, Neil Lowden, Ray Tosser, Nick Cresswell, ALICE & LAURIE O'CONNOR, Jenni Cowdy, Stephanie Lee Brown, Lord Ruddy Wood Esq (David), Graff-City.Com, Big Gay Benny, Paul Abbott, Colin McAlinden, the impoSt!, Daniel Cavanagh, Pauly & Sarah Surridge, Matt Lucock, Dan Locke, Matt "Another one?" Jackson, Adrian Sheehan, Harvey Powell, Mike Savage gets dicked around by Cathy Russell, The Stone Twins, Sean Wilson, Pete "Griff" Griffiths, The Allskips, Nathan Allison, Miss '65' Roberts & Joe '99' G, Lloyd Evans, Capt Alexander Hood, Dr Craig Campbell, the Hon. Dafydd Malcolm, Andy Blow, Robin "Room 5" Woodward, Michael Lobb, Saq Rasul, Owen Evans, Ben Chadwick, Matt Fairhall, Ruth "just got hitched" Croney, Matthew Keen, Emma Orr, Richard Morgan, Ant, Anna & Sonny, David "gamingdave" Robinson, Danny Crump, Alex Fraser, Cap'n Billy Firebeard, Steve Rye, Stefan Fafinski, Jake Zak's dad, Jamie Keddie, Matthew Cattee, Dave, Karen, Lily and Annie High, Tod Hunter, Dave High, Mat Eames, Rob Greb, The Tolleys, Nick Marsh, jude emmanuel brown, Dave Pullig, Neil Cook, Dave Johnson, Philip John, Jonathan "synth boy" Stephens, Sarah Watt, Simon Long, BoogaLouCipher, Tom & Val Raworth, Dave Oldfield, mark fowell, Joanna Statham, Le Ginge, Anna Groot, Matthew Jones, Darryl Smith, Iain "Like a Boss" Wilson, Dean Pearce, Bob Pullen (Maggy Cant), Mr Robert Dawes MEng, Vinny the Bear, Dougie Rothnie, Mankauf, Belen Lopez, Simon Keith Neal yeah?, Ian 'Humpty' Humphreys, la fabulista, Russell "Rusty" Dean, Robin Barnard, Mr Fred Forse, Sarah 'coates' Wright innit, Lord Adam of Stratfink, Jamie Hancock, Rob Williams, WOOLEY GROMIT, Nick Who Hasn't Paid His Speaking Tax Lenz & His Lardship Matt Baish Lord of Greggs, Peter Murray, Sheffield's Finest, Jonny Hall, Paul S J Martin, Kate Lewis, Chris York, Nick Lewis, Jenny Norman, Ben Finn, Rob Cunting Halloway, Nicky NoLongerPierghetto Wifelet, Chris BUYING MORE SHIT Sharman, Zoe Richmond-Smith, Grant Philpott, Ben Hultum, ochre7, Thomas' Le Cock' Crompton, David Frettsome, Julia East, Ross Neary, Kelly Hubbs & James Ross, Richard this is the 7th damn book I've bought from you Paul-Jones, Ben Neary, Mark Rivers, Neil Overett, Samantha Veal, Big Ben from Tallinn!, Posh Will, Charlotte Fairbairn, Paul Thomsen Kirk, Karl de Vroomen, Charles Wander, Neil Barnett, Alan you wanker, Ben "Can't Think Of Anything Funny" J, Marcus the Kiwi, Michele the Legal Longshot, Gareth Barton, Tommy Day, Ra and the Pisswizards of Greewich, David Grievson, Anne Martin, Jolyon Gobshite, Archbishop of Canterbury, Eggwald Wigglesworth Runnerteer , Stuart Collins, Ed Webber, Stewart 'Alex' Killala, Paul Cross, Justin Mason, Sam, David & Helen, Dan Augey thinks Jenna Willis is an effin gobshite that just bangs on about Aqua Pets all fucking day long on twitter. Hi Royal, love you, Andy Ibbotson, Mark Hewis, Yeah, my name's LUTZ STOEVER, Kevin Richardson, Claire Elise Everitt, Kate Creature, Steve Matthews, Neil Cocklin, Marcus 'Fat Chad' Chadwick, Phil Williams, Ian Coburn, smackdee, Simon Ozzy Osment, Doug Huggins, Ant 'I read it on the shitter' Farmer, Tristan Ash, Big Jamesy, Demetrius Breedlove Kemp, Alex 'the chimp' Layton, Elaine "Naughty Girl" Gill aka Splodge, Henry 'The Brunes' Russell, Nick Kenny, Harrison Fox, Matt Guy, Jonathan Privett , Ian Funnell, BJSOLO, Richard Grievson, Fraser Mann, Jez Light, Mearsy, Saul Taylor, Matt Bayfield, Mark Wheatley, TallBitchSazzle, Sean & Tanya, Peter Halliwell, Thomas O'Loughlin, Sandra Ishkanes, Bin Gibson (it's Mrs), Duncan Cook, FlyingDutchman, Felicity Reardon, Miss Anne Jackson, Alan Lim, Alan Harrington, Joe and Sam Wicks, Winchy, Mark West, Iain "IT'S ALL A BIT BOLLOCKS" Wareham, jaslovestonyhadley, Philip Suggars & Zoe Porteous, Kirsty Super-MacKenzie, Alan Smallwood, Simon "some sort of cunt" Arnold, Mattie, Samantha Tang, Benjamin John Holt of *THE MIGHTY RUFUS*, Caroline Sykes, Kevin McClenaghan, the boy Crump, Anne, Stevie & Eleanor Curran - on the potty, yeah?, DOPSKOP, Chris Smithies, The Kissousaurus, Rossy & Kate-Pac, Luke Miller, Martin Ruddy, Jukka Kurkela, Rob Ford, Gary Watt, Danny O'Hare, Rob Bailey, Neil "Tango" Tandy, Vish, Di Walker, Kiran Khetia, Mr & Mrs Hickey, Dulcie Mustafah Ball, Soph Lucinda Whittaker, Adam Rickart, To my second illegitimate son, Toby Victorio, Small Faces Mikey Hurn, Karina Mitchell, Niall Gault, Tennille "I want a claw-foot bath" Burnside, Ciaran Flynn, Rich Chad Chamley, STEPHEN "Donkey-Splasher" MARTIN, Rich Parsons, Darren Startup, Miho Ohta, John Cunt Esq., David Varden, Em the weeblebeeder, Martin "arsepipe" Price yeah, Steven Kehoe, Sarah Maxey, Frank Bauer, Vive la République, Julian Milne, Dr Hitler Hugh, Dr Sasha Strangelove, Baby Fenner, "johnnyapples", JASON T TYNAN, The Mighty Jarv, Peter Reay, Robertsone, Shrek and Lem, Tooney, Gary Thomas Ball, JOE GRIFFIN, Paul Gregson, Andy Tough, Jaimini Jani, Stuart 'You got a problem with that?' Wilson, Chris Plumley, Grace Hannigan, Jim Goodwin, Anna (I like Alan the monster though I'm only 2) Osborne, Bertie Jennings, Alison Crinion, Jamie McCall, MARMOSET!, Miss Mon, Bronwen Eldridge (age 50), Twink Addison, Dan Waring, Matthieu Rolland, Abigail Swallow, Emma Crompton, Sargeant Farmer, Tim Havard, Helen Marquis, Ian Hunter, bazzalee, Andy 'Malignant Cunt' Fernandez, Jack Basey Wilkinson, Chris Littlejohn, Jason Panudy, Zachary 'Writer Boy' Colbert, Dr Simon Clough, Nick Rosewarne, Meester Bond, Lord JAYLEEEEN, PRINCESS CLAIRE BAAAAAERT, Geordie Coxon Yeah ?, Andrew Carlin, Neil "Neilson Piquet" Parker, johnnie ladyboy tubthumper, angela cheese wig, Joel Nesbitt, Steve Eastaugh-Waring, Drew Rogers, Damien Warburton, Sir Boderick Mittens the third, Shane, Matilda's Dad, yeah?, THE FUCKING SINGER OFF VOICE OF REASON, Geraint Rogers, Jammy Strickens, DONQY JON LAMING, Sam, Dwight Spiegelhacker, George Salmon, Gary Worley, Gareth Gamble, Canon J Who, Adrian Worman, Jordan

Speed, Jonathan Reason, Jodie "you alright with that yeah?" Edgson, Paul 'DonkeySpank' Hancock, Ben Golding, Roy Thirlwall, Rob Tamlin, Sammy Davies, Julien Aujeau, Simon Long, John Peter Gilbert, Oz Owen, Richard Utter Tosser Morris, Barry Nicholson, Christopher Parry, David Harkin, William Harry Jerrold, yeah, Bob BK, Stu "The Tattoo" Camm, Chris Jackson, Lynsey Sutcliffe, Chris Walker, ray moody, AndyJFuckIKEA, Dan Harrison, Matt Evans, Louis Devitt, Adam Teeuw, YourLocalGP, Jonathan Miles, Alex Jolliffe, Florence Wylde Raworth, Arthur Husk, Tom Stubbs, The Cunts Marshall-Nicholls, Kevin Lowrie, Michael Bennett, Phil Ashworth, Kettle Witch, Sam & Claire "See How Mi Sexy" Grantham, Luca Galbiati, Draper Davey, We might give this to Mark Muir for Christmas, Cunt Juice De Bosco, Martin France, Martin Shithouse Gaylord Galvin, Liz Tollfree, MIKE STAFFORD IN CAPITALS, The Chelms', Chantal Colson, Terrance del Fuego, Boooohoooohoooon, Dr Rhys H Thomas BSc, MBChB, MRCP, Simon winter, chris dorward, Ben Gould, Rowan Chernin, Kevin McDougall, Jenny Pennington, Tanya Paice, Oliver Perritt, Craig T Jackson, Ronan Burns, James Fenn, Calum Gordon, Antony B Silson, Chris & Elif, Gregory Burton, Phil & Kate Whaite, Francesca Moore, Geoffrey I Sproule, Gunnar Eigener, Stephen Cunningham, George Crackers, Alison Walster Yeah?, Scott *kiss me* Hardy, Simon Cochrane, Jake "The Owl-botherer" Williams, Adam Jameson, TIGGSY & MONKS WAS 'ERE, Julia 'The Kraken' Perris, Neil & Vicky, Simon Rees, Colin Boyter, Cliff Bambridge, Jonathan Vine, Jennifer & Patrick Clyder, Dean Feebery, Hazel E Newton, Alistair Reith, Richard Pedrick, Simon James Smith, Knightsyopps, Didi van Antwerpen, Joe Freeman, Glen "Elmo Putney" Edwards, Graeme Langlands, Kristan Harbut, Steve Pape, Mike Surman & The Naked Beatles, Michael Graham Thomas, Russell Graham, Aled Rogers, Deb Southwold, Tifrahat & co., Dame Edith Poopy, Bru the Cunt, Faye Brimson, Iain H, Edmund "James Caan you belched" Monk, Paul Jackman, Nick Parker-Groom, John Bentham, Steve Hayward, Stephen Gray, Ian Goldsmith, Garrett Pantyraid, Simon & Claire Hunter, Pauline Golds, Lizzie Walker, Tom O'Brien, Dave Abrahams, Nigel & Christine Driver, Adrian Brett Kieran Brett Dominic Brett, That cunt from RSJ, Ewan G Hepburn, Duncan A Hepburn, Rob Honeybone, Tim Roberts, jo Jeffery, Kathy Taylor, Pig, Matt Upchuck, Hello to Kevin Hill, Ben Halliwell, Simon Stevenson Cowan, Jon & Natasha Fielden, Helen & Gabs, MAtT 'Ahote' WilSOn As iT's WRitTeN FoR OnCe PleaSE, Stuart "Ianto" Evans, Sir Charles MacDonald, Big J Masters, Leonardo 'Hotsteppa" Pepper, Mark Wiseman, Akira Samata, benwithpen, lil' kels and sam spacey, David and Joanne Hoskin-Linn, Steve Routley, Edric, Rachel Palmer, Barry Goshawk, Tony Morley, Ben Winbolt-Lewis, Thomasina, Nick-Mate, Sino-Mikro!, Barrie Hemsley, Kev the Twisted Animator, Tootles Woodstock Chamberlain, Iain Panda Robertson, Disko Briscoe - I'm a bit bored..., Andy "geographically somewhat removed" McDonnell, Rob Close, Pete Wood, Katharyn Lanaro, Andy Hough, Joseph millen, Christoffejay, Karl&Michelle Wareham, Gary McConnell, Adrian Worman, Eric Mitchell, Mac Daddy McBride, Neal 'Beautiful Eyes' McLaughlin, ROO Rennik LEWIS, Hazel and Phil, Wilfred George Boone, Helen Marsden, Nigel Sheehan, Adrian Hardwick, Laura Curme, Johnny Blonde, Stuart 'bad man' Curme , Jazzy Drop Stolk, SIR MARTIN J MORETTI OBE, Mike Currie, Steve Wrench are ya?, Simon "Fuck Your Job" Bond, Alice Smith, Kunt, JAMES TWEEDIE YEAH?, Elaine 'tiny dancer' Bloor, Candice 'your mum failed' Blackwell, Widiane "Chico" O'Moussa, Shane Murphy, Chris Ford, Bean Counter, @THOMASROBOT McCUNTY, Errol Allen Tyler, Charlie "Manus" Hutton, DirtyKestrel, Michael "Baby Daddy" Blay, Oliver Creamer, Steven McDade, Mike stuffandsense.com Lee, Jo Worsfold, Kate Halton, Nick Waddington, liamcuntingfranklin, Stu & Becky Swift, Geoff de Jeff Jeff and chips and Clairepops, Spendo, Alex Kickham, Ant Brett, Ken Evil, Professor Wilson "He's Not A Sweetie, HE'S A CUNT!!!" MacMillan, John Coop, James Murphy, Nicola Newman, Bina Piggywig, John Ashworth, Simon Zinc Trumpet Harris, Josh Harwood, Joe Phelan, Laura 'Ladywood' Oakes, David Lee, frances Madell, Sebastian Walker, Woodsy, Fraser fuckin looks like it Clarke, Luke R Sneddon, Dan Harwood, Joe Chapman, Nicholas Swann, Daniel Todaro & Simon Durrant, Robin Cordina, lee Ford, Hayden Wood, James Matthews, Chris Packham, Daniel Spaniel, Joe Hall, Don't say no to panda, Simon Sharville, Stephos & Lucebot, James "got your name in here again, eh?" Clarke, Jonathan Mason, Simon "is a poisonous little raspberry" Hurrell, Jazzman George and LouLou, James Robinson, Olly O'Conor, Mark Maplethorpe, Meg Price, sorry I forgot your birthday Jono, Chris Naughton, Richard 'Grey Dog' Hart, Matt Rookestar, Shaun Atkinson, Superbreaker, Bubula Fanta Pants, jezmaw, James Nadin, Frankie ""MOONFACE"" Buckle, Richard Wig Harris, Martin Smith, Robin Evans, Mark Vose, tim wedlake, Gemma Newbery and Jonny Wilcox, Richard Kew, Julie Stewart, James Smyth, Vernon Authers yeah, Paul Moulton, Jack 'Jack Dee' Dee, Dave 'Big Gay Dave' Triff, Glynn W. Clarkson, Matthew John Tassell, Karmer Karl, Ryan Cool, DFR Av, Jon Bremner, Richard "Finchley Central Market" Tarrant, Mike Ashworth, vickyblue, Richard Jukes, Milo Fadite, Stan Swallow, David "Badger" Heiland, Chris Rothwell, Lee West, Christopher e Holden, Katrina KP Maier, Oli Harrex, Schmoo & Qwoo, Henrietta "People Skills" Cuntrag, Nik Bridge, Emma Sutherland, Jon and Mike @stuffandsense.com, Thom Snufkin Allen, James A. McMurray, Jonathan Knowles, Thoma Carratt, oh personality Scriv, Mac, Graham Scott, james Goulding, Debbie Sharman, BlobOfMark, Sarah Stewart, stephanie hinton, Euan Tulloch, Peter Noah Jack Dingwall, Mr M J M OBE, Michael Purnell, Matthias Stokes, Ann Dunstan, Martin Root, Rich & Cath, Tom Knight, SiKehoe, Barge Forward Crew E14 Lynn, Jake & Olivia, PHIL CASS, Richard Black, Samuel J Smith and Family, Paul "prostate in a jar" Davies, Ash Wood, Grant Bissett, Alan Gray, Phil Lee, Alan Ashley, Ratman & Bobbin, David Mills, John de Pear, Minton, Danny Amey, kate Corbin, Paul Jackson, Alex Dennis, Michael Prince, Rosie Soulman, Marcus Thomas, Victoria Goddard, Strumski, Chris Mccaffrey, Matt Payne, Tez & Wendy - 2 massive twats, Come back Fay, you wanker!, Steve Hill, Ricjard Rhodes, Matthew SHERIDAN, Uncle Daddy Matt Lynch, Cliff Hendry, George D Tomlinson, Matt Ware, Bertie von Brimmers, Robyn Llewellyn, Elisa Parish, Diane Browne, Nigel King, Robert Jones, James Hunt, Anthony Babajee.